CONGRATULATIONS GRADUATE

Guest Book

_____

NAME

_____

SCHOOL

_____

DATE & LOCATION

D1416437

We are so proud of you!

CLASS of 2022

CONGRATULATIONS GRADUATE

Name _____

Happy Thoughts

_____
_____
_____
_____
_____
_____

_____
_____
_____
_____

Life Advice

CLASS of 2022

CONGRATULATIONS GRADUATE

Name _____

Happy Thoughts

Life Advice

CLASS of 2022

CONGRATULATIONS GRADUATE

Name

Happy Thoughts

Life Advice

CLASS of 2022

CONGRATULATIONS GRADUATE

Name _____

Happy Thoughts

_____
_____
_____
_____
_____
_____
_____
_____
_____
_____

Life Advice

CLASS of 2022

CONGRATULATIONS GRADUATE

Name _____

Happy Thoughts

_____
_____
_____
_____
_____
_____

_____
_____
_____
_____
_____

Life Advice

CLASS of 2022

CONGRATULATIONS GRADUATE

Name _____

Happy Thoughts

_____
_____
_____
_____
_____
_____

_____
_____
_____
_____
_____

Life Advice

CLASS of 2022

CONGRATULATIONS GRADUATE

Name _____

Happy Thoughts

_____
_____
_____
_____
_____

_____
_____
_____
_____

Life Advice

CLASS of 2022

CONGRATULATIONS GRADUATE

Name _____

Happy Thoughts

_____
_____
_____
_____
_____
_____

_____
_____
_____
_____

Life Advice

CLASS of 2022

CONGRATULATIONS
GRADUATE

Name _____

Happy Thoughts

_____
_____
_____
_____
_____
_____

_____
_____
_____
_____
_____
_____

Life Advice

CLASS
of 2022

CONGRATULATIONS GRADUATE

Name _____

Happy Thoughts

_____
_____
_____
_____
_____
_____

_____
_____
_____
_____

Life Advice

CLASS of 2022

CONGRATULATIONS GRADUATE

Name _____

Happy Thoughts

Life Advice

CLASS of 2022

CONGRATULATIONS GRADUATE

Name _____

Happy Thoughts

_____
_____
_____
_____
_____
_____
_____
_____
_____
_____
_____
_____
_____

Life Advice

CLASS of 2022

CONGRATULATIONS GRADUATE

Name _____

Happy Thoughts

_____
_____
_____
_____
_____
_____

_____
_____
_____
_____
_____

Life Advice

CLASS of 2022

CONGRATULATIONS GRADUATE

Name _____

Happy Thoughts

Life Advice

CLASS of 2022

CONGRATULATIONS GRADUATE

Name _____

Happy Thoughts

_____
_____
_____
_____
_____
_____

_____
_____
_____
_____

Life Advice

CLASS of 2022

CONGRATULATIONS GRADUATE

Name _____

Happy Thoughts

Life Advice

CLASS of 2022

CONGRATULATIONS GRADUATE

Name _____

Happy Thoughts

_____
_____
_____
_____
_____
_____

_____
_____
_____
_____

Life Advice

CLASS of 2022

CONGRATULATIONS
GRADUATE

Name _____

Happy Thoughts

_____
_____
_____
_____
_____
_____

_____
_____
_____
_____

Life Advice

CLASS
of
2022

CONGRATULATIONS
GRADUATE

Name _____

Happy Thoughts

Life Advice

CLASS of 2022

CONGRATULATIONS GRADUATE

Name _____

Happy Thoughts

Life Advice

CLASS of 2022

CONGRATULATIONS GRADUATE

Name _____

Happy Thoughts

_____
_____
_____
_____
_____
_____

_____
_____
_____
_____
_____

Life Advice

CLASS of 2022

CONGRATULATIONS GRADUATE

Name _____

Happy Thoughts

_____

_____

_____

_____

_____

_____

_____

_____

_____

Life Advice

CLASS of 2022

CONGRATULATIONS
GRADUATE

Name _____

Happy Thoughts

Life Advice

CLASS of 2022

CONGRATULATIONS GRADUATE

Name _____

Happy Thoughts

_____
_____
_____
_____
_____
_____
_____

_____
_____
_____
_____
_____

Life Advice

CLASS of 2022

CONGRATULATIONS
GRADUATE

Name _____

Happy Thoughts

_____
_____
_____
_____
_____
_____

_____
_____
_____
_____

Life Advice

CLASS *of* 2022

CONGRATULATIONS
GRADUATE

Name _____

Happy Thoughts

Life Advice

CLASS of 2022

CONGRATULATIONS
GRADUATE

Name

Happy Thoughts

Life Advice

CLASS of 2022

CONGRATULATIONS
GRADUATE

Name _____

Happy Thoughts

Life Advice

CLASS of 2022

CONGRATULATIONS
GRADUATE

Name _____

Happy Thoughts

_____
_____
_____
_____
_____

_____
_____
_____
_____
_____

Life Advice

CLASS of 2022

CONGRATULATIONS
GRADUATE

Name _____

Happy Thoughts

_____
_____
_____
_____
_____
_____

_____
_____
_____
_____
_____

Life Advice

CLASS of 2022

CONGRATULATIONS GRADUATE

Name _____

Happy Thoughts

_____
_____
_____
_____
_____

_____
_____
_____
_____

Life Advice

CLASS of 2022

CONGRATULATIONS
GRADUATE

Name _____

Happy Thoughts

_____

_____

_____

_____

_____

_____

_____

_____

_____

Life Advice

CLASS of 2022

CONGRATULATIONS
GRADUATE

Name _____

Happy Thoughts

Life Advice

CLASS of 2022

CONGRATULATIONS
GRADUATE

Name

Happy Thoughts

Life Advice

CLASS
of
2022

CONGRATULATIONS GRADUATE

Name _____

Happy Thoughts

_____
_____
_____
_____
_____
_____

_____
_____
_____
_____

Life Advice

CLASS of 2022

CONGRATULATIONS GRADUATE

Name _____

Happy Thoughts

_____

_____

_____

_____

_____

_____

_____

_____

Life Advice

CLASS of 2022

CONGRATULATIONS GRADUATE

Name _____

Happy Thoughts

Life Advice

CLASS of 2022

CONGRATULATIONS GRADUATE

Name _____

Happy Thoughts

_____
_____
_____
_____
_____
_____

_____
_____
_____
_____

Life Advice

CLASS of 2022

CONGRATULATIONS GRADUATE

Name _____

Happy Thoughts

_____
_____
_____
_____
_____

_____
_____
_____
_____
_____

Life Advice

CLASS of 2022

CONGRATULATIONS
GRADUATE

Name _____

Happy Thoughts

_____
_____
_____
_____
_____
_____

_____
_____
_____
_____
_____

Life Advice

CLASS of 2022

CONGRATULATIONS GRADUATE

Name _____

Happy Thoughts

_____
_____
_____
_____
_____
_____

_____
_____
_____
_____

Life Advice

CLASS of 2022

CONGRATULATIONS
GRADUATE

Name _____

Happy Thoughts

_____
_____
_____
_____
_____
_____

_____
_____
_____
_____
_____

Life Advice

CLASS
of
2022

CONGRATULATIONS GRADUATE

Name _____

Happy Thoughts

_____
_____
_____
_____
_____
_____

_____
_____
_____
_____
_____

Life Advice

CLASS of 2022

CONGRATULATIONS GRADUATE

Name _____

Happy Thoughts

_____
_____
_____
_____
_____
_____
_____
_____
_____
_____
_____

Life Advice

CLASS of 2022

CONGRATULATIONS GRADUATE

Name _____

Happy Thoughts

_____
_____
_____
_____
_____

_____
_____
_____
_____

Life Advice

CLASS of 2022

CONGRATULATIONS
GRADUATE

Name _____

Happy Thoughts

_____
_____
_____
_____
_____

_____
_____
_____
_____
_____

Life Advice

CLASS
of
2022

CONGRATULATIONS GRADUATE

Name _____

_____
_____
_____
_____
_____
_____

Happy Thoughts

_____
_____
_____
_____

Life Advice

CLASS of 2022

CONGRATULATIONS GRADUATE

Name _____

Happy Thoughts

_____
_____
_____
_____
_____

_____
_____
_____
_____
_____

Life Advice

CLASS of 2022

CONGRATULATIONS GRADUATE

Name _____

Happy Thoughts

_____
_____
_____
_____
_____
_____

_____
_____
_____
_____
_____

Life Advice

CLASS of 2022

CONGRATULATIONS GRADUATE

Name _____

Happy Thoughts

_____
_____
_____
_____
_____
_____

_____
_____
_____
_____
_____

Life Advice

CLASS of 2022

CONGRATULATIONS GRADUATE

Name _____

Happy Thoughts

_____
_____
_____
_____
_____
_____
_____
_____
_____
_____

Life Advice

CLASS of 2022

CONGRATULATIONS GRADUATE

Name _____

Happy Thoughts

_____
_____
_____
_____
_____
_____

_____
_____
_____
_____
_____

Life Advice

CLASS of 2022

CONGRATULATIONS GRADUATE

Name _____

Happy Thoughts

_____

_____

_____

_____

_____

_____

_____

_____

_____

Life Advice

CLASS of 2022

CONGRATULATIONS GRADUATE

Name _____

Happy Thoughts

_____
_____
_____
_____
_____

_____
_____
_____
_____
_____

Life Advice

CLASS of 2022

CONGRATULATIONS
GRADUATE

Name _____

Happy Thoughts

Life Advice

CLASS of 2022

CONGRATULATIONS
GRADUATE

Name _____

Happy Thoughts

Life Advice

CLASS *of* 2022

CONGRATULATIONS GRADUATE

Name _____

Happy Thoughts

_____
_____
_____
_____
_____
_____

_____
_____
_____
_____

Life Advice

CLASS of 2022

CONGRATULATIONS GRADUATE

Name _____

Happy Thoughts

_____
_____
_____
_____
_____

_____
_____
_____
_____
_____

Life Advice

CLASS of 2022

CONGRATULATIONS
GRADUATE

Name _____

Happy Thoughts

_____
_____
_____
_____
_____

_____
_____
_____
_____

Life Advice

CLASS *of* 2022

CONGRATULATIONS GRADUATE

Name _____

Happy Thoughts

Life Advice

CLASS of 2022

CONGRATULATIONS GRADUATE

Name _____

Happy Thoughts

_____
_____
_____
_____
_____
_____

_____
_____
_____
_____
_____

Life Advice

CLASS of 2022

CONGRATULATIONS GRADUATE

Name

Happy Thoughts

Life Advice

CLASS of 2022

CONGRATULATIONS
GRADUATE

Name _____

Happy Thoughts

_____

_____

_____

_____

_____

_____

_____

_____

_____

_____

Life Advice

CLASS of 2022

CONGRATULATIONS GRADUATE

Name _____

Happy Thoughts

_____
_____
_____
_____
_____

_____
_____
_____
_____

Life Advice

CLASS of 2022

CONGRATULATIONS GRADUATE

Name _____

Happy Thoughts

_____
_____
_____
_____
_____
_____

_____
_____
_____
_____
_____

Life Advice

CLASS of 2022

CONGRATULATIONS GRADUATE

Name _____

Happy Thoughts

Life Advice

CLASS of 2022

CONGRATULATIONS
GRADUATE

Name _____

Happy Thoughts

_____
_____
_____
_____
_____
_____

_____
_____
_____
_____

Life Advice

CLASS of 2022

CONGRATULATIONS GRADUATE

Name _____

Happy Thoughts

_____
_____
_____
_____
_____

_____
_____
_____
_____

Life Advice

CLASS of 2022

CONGRATULATIONS GRADUATE

Name

Happy Thoughts

Life Advice

CLASS of 2022

CONGRATULATIONS GRADUATE

Name _____

Happy Thoughts

Life Advice

CLASS of 2022

CONGRATULATIONS GRADUATE

Name

Happy Thoughts

Life Advice

CLASS of 2022

CONGRATULATIONS GRADUATE

Name _____

Happy Thoughts

_____
_____
_____
_____
_____
_____
_____
_____
_____

Life Advice

CLASS of 2022

CONGRATULATIONS
GRADUATE

Name _____

Happy Thoughts

Life Advice

CLASS of 2022

CONGRATULATIONS GRADUATE

Name _____

Happy Thoughts

_____
_____
_____
_____
_____
_____

_____
_____
_____
_____

Life Advice

CLASS of 2022

Gift Log

Name

Gift

Gift Log

Name   Gift

_____   _____
_____   _____
_____   _____
_____   _____
_____   _____
_____   _____
_____   _____
_____   _____
_____   _____
_____   _____
_____   _____
_____   _____

Gift Log

Name

Gift

CONGRATULATIONS GRADUATE

Gift Log

Name

Gift

_____

_____

_____

_____

_____

_____

_____

_____

_____

_____

CLASS of 2022

Gift Log

Name	Gift
_____	_____
_____	_____
_____	_____
_____	_____
_____	_____
_____	_____
_____	_____
_____	_____
_____	_____
_____	_____
_____	_____

CLASS
of
2022